Baby Animals

Parents' Guide

My Baby Animals Poster Book includes beautiful photo posters—and illustrations for your child to color. You'll also find interesting facts about the baby animals we feature. Here are some ways to enhance your child's learning and enjoyment.

Read together
Read the book aloud and talk about the animals pictured. This exchange helps develop your child's listening skills and imagination.

Make it personal
Invite your child to experiment with color and add to the drawings. This encourages self-expression and builds critical thinking skills.

Offer options
Provide a mix of materials: crayons, markers, paints, stickers. Manipulating art materials develops skills needed for reading and writing.

Talk about it
Ask your child to tell you about the end result. This is an opportunity to practice social skills, and it supports language development.

DUCKLING

Ducklings like tall grass. It helps them hide and is home to bugs they eat. Draw more grass and a few friends to hide with this duckling.

Easy extras
• Set out ingredients, such as rice, pasta, and beans, and let your child glue them on drawings to add texture or create a mosaic.

• Layer different materials to enhance the tactile experience. After coloring, your child can attach yarn or fabric, finger paint over the coloring, or simply add glitter or stickers.

• Turn household items into art tools. Paint with cotton swabs or sponges, or blow on drops of paint with a drinking straw.

Beyond the book
• Have older children shoot their own photos, then make drawings based on them.

• Take the book to your local zoo and see how many of the pictured animals you can find.

• Learn more about animals by taking a research trip to the library, by looking online, or by watching educational programs.

• Seek out animal museums and art exhibits. Remember to bring a sketch book!

LAMB

A lamb's fur is called fleece. When a lamb gets a haircut, the fleece is made into wool. To give your lamb extra soft fleece, glue on some soft cloth or cotton.

ZEBRA FOAL

Real zebras have black and white stripes, but yours can have stripes in any color.
You can also glue on newspaper or wrapping paper to give it a different pattern.

RABBIT KIT

Baby bunnies will begin to nibble on solid food as early as 2 weeks of age.
Is this kit standing up for a snack? Draw a carrot or other treat for it.

BLACK BEAR CUB

A bear weighs only about a pound at birth, but it can grow as large as 500 pounds.
This cub still looks pretty light! Connect the dots to finish the cub and the tree.

Marmosets are small monkeys that live in jungles. This marmoset is smelling a flower. Can you think of other things it might see and smell in the jungle?

Elephants bathe in mud because it keeps them cool and protects them from biting insects. Will there be bugs in your drawing? How about a bright sun?

Most horse foals are born at night. Their mothers like the dark for privacy.
Do you want to make it night or day in your drawing?

PENGUIN CHICK

Penguin chicks have soft feathers that are later replaced with adult feathers.
After you connect the dots, color the feathers any way you would like.

Ring-tailed lemurs have hands with fingers and thumbs, just like yours. Draw something for this lemur to hold: maybe a piece of fruit, one of its favorite foods.

After you connect the dots, you'll see two black-tailed prairie dogs.
In real life, the tips of their tails are black, but you can make yours any color.

BABY CROCODILE

Baby crocodiles are covered with tough scales that help protect them. Draw scales of any shape you would like on this baby crocodile.

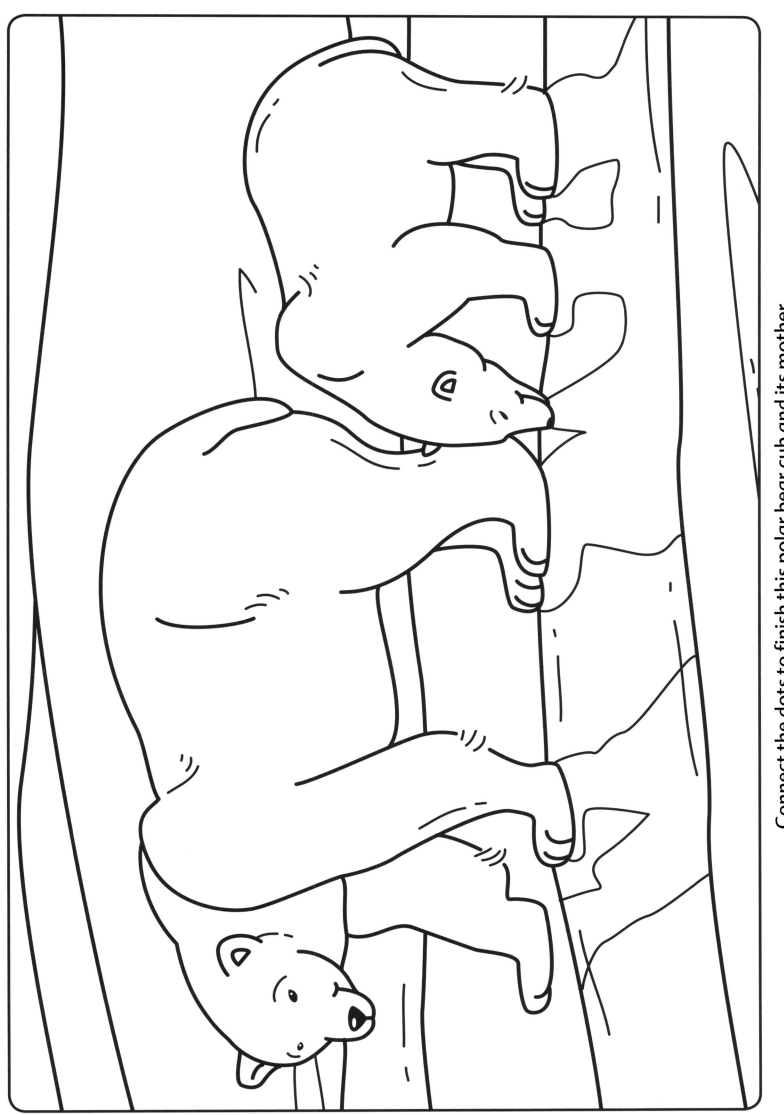

Connect the dots to finish this polar bear cub and its mother.
Although polar bears' fur appears white or tan, their hair is actually clear.

DUCKLING

Ducklings like tall grass. It helps them hide and is home to bugs they eat.
Draw more grass and a few friends to hide with this duckling.

Lions are social cats. That means they like to hang out with each other.
This cub is resting with its father. How does your family spend time together?

CALF

A calf needs to eat lots of grass and drink milk to grow from 60 pounds at birth to 1,000 pounds or more. Draw some grass for this calf to eat.

Once you connect the dots, you will see a harp seal lying in the snow. Its fur is thick to protect it from the snow and white to help it hide from larger animals.

A tiger's stripes help it blend into its surroundings.
Can you color the background to help this tiger cub hide?

A baby whitetail deer is called a fawn. It is born with spots that help it hide from larger animals. Add more spots to help the fawn hide.

KOALA JOEY

Koalas live in trees in Australia. A baby koala rides from tree to tree on its mother's back. Where do you like to go with your mother?

PIGLET

A group of piglets born on the same day is called a litter. A litter can have as many as 12 piglets. Draw some of this piglet's brothers and sisters.

ORANGUTAN INFANT

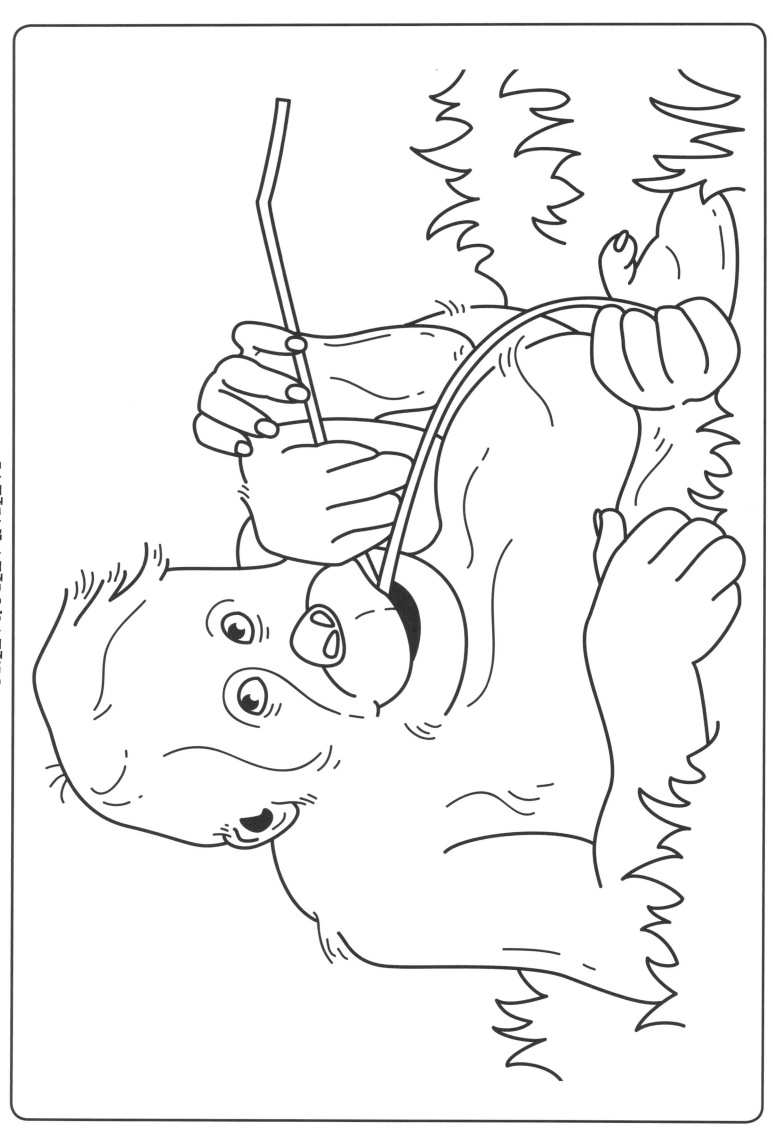

Orangutans' feet are like hands. They can grasp and climb with their toes. This one is holding a piece of straw. Draw other things for this infant to grab.

BUSH DUIKER CALF

Bush duikers are small African antelopes with long legs.
Connect the dots to finish this calf. Calves can run within hours of birth!

PANDA CUB

Pandas lie on their backs because it makes it easier for them to hold things like bamboo, their favorite food. What's this panda holding?

Macaques are small, intelligent monkeys that love to climb trees.
Draw some leaves and branches to finish the tree for this macaque.

LION CUB

Lion cubs need lots of rest so they have energy to play and practice hunting skills. What is this cub dreaming?

Wild goats live on steep mountains. They are natural climbers with good balance.
Where are these goats climbing? On a mountain? In the clouds?

DONKEY FOAL

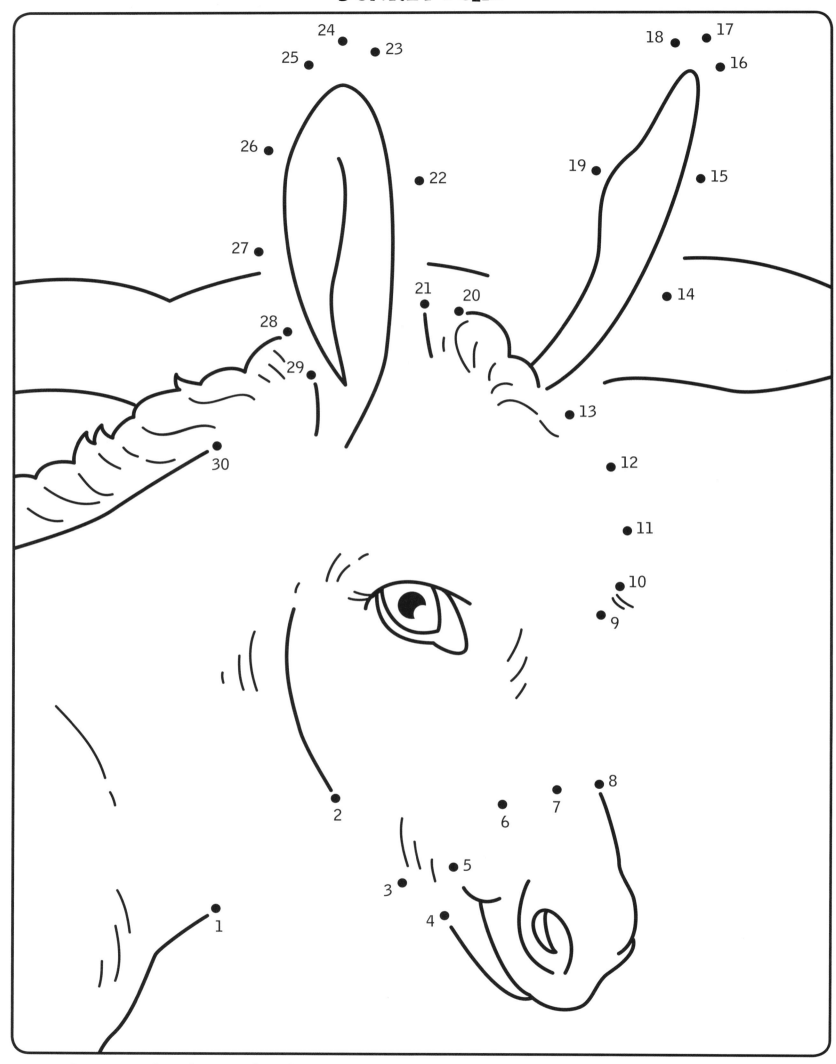

Connect the dots to finish the donkey foal's large ears. Donkeys use their ears to listen for special sounds like the bray, the loud sound other donkeys make.

GIRAFFE FOAL

Giraffes are the tallest animals on Earth. A newborn is six feet tall!
Giraffes are known for their patches. What pattern will you draw on this giraffe?

The red fox pups are playing in their house, which is called a den.
You can glue on paper, bark, or cloth to decorate their den if you would like.

White tigers aren't usually pure white—most have visible stripes, and they all have blue eyes and pink noses. What colors will you make this cub?

Getting to know baby animals

STARTING OUT Some baby animals, like bear cubs, do all of their growing inside of their moms before they are born. Other babies grow inside eggs that their mothers lay. Penguin chicks incubate in eggs for 9 weeks before they are ready to hatch.

FAMILIES Sometimes baby animals are born on the same day as their brothers and sisters. Most fox mothers give birth to three or four kits, and twins are common for mountain goat moms. Horse foals are usually born just one at a time.

FIRST STEPS Zebra foals can walk within minutes of being born, but it takes koala cubs longer to get started. Immediately after birth, they go into their mothers' pouches, where they stay protected for the next 5—7 months.

LOOK-ALIKE Polar bear cubs basically look like smaller versions of their parents, but baby ducklings have a very different appearance from adults. Their looks change a lot as they grow.

READY, SET, GROW It's important that baby animals eat a nutritious diet because they need fuel for all of the growing they have to do. Baby animals can grow very fast—rabbit kits and piglets can double in weight in their first week.

AT HOME Baby animals live in all kinds of places. Duck, elephant, and deer families like tall grass, macaques and koala bears live high up in the trees, and prairie dogs make their homes in underground tunnels.

MOVING OUT Some baby animals, like bears, tigers, and penguins, stay with their moms until they are ready to go out on their own. Others, like baby crocodiles, are ready to fend for themselves as soon as they are born.

A day in the life . . .

EAT Some baby animals, like ducks and penguins, eat the same foods as their parents. Other babies start with just milk from their mothers.

SLEEP Like human babies, many baby animals spend a lot of time asleep. While they sleep, they are growing strong muscles and bones.

TALK Many baby animals make special sounds to communicate and help their parents keep track of them. A penguin's mom can pick out her chick's voice from a crowd of hundreds.

WASH UP Lion and fox parents bathe their babies, licking them until they are clean. Other baby animals, like seal pups, don't need much help. They just jump right into the water!

PLAY Baby animals learn very important skills, like jumping and climbing, through play. The exercise also helps them grow strong.